Tom has a big bag full of bricks.

He tips the bag up. The bricks land on the mat.

Tom plays with the bricks.

He has a castle on the mat.

3

'Can I play with the bricks?' says Bella.

'You can play with the green bricks,' says Tom.

Bella picks up the bricks
and puts them in the bag.

She bends down to get
the last green brick.

Oh no! The castle! Tom is cross. Bella is sorry.